"When we set out to create a community of technical scholars in Silicon Valley, there wasn't much here, and the rest of the world looked awfully big. Now a lot of the rest of the world is here."

FREDERICK TERMAN

Considered one of the "Fathers of Silicon Valley"

(1900-1982)

HELLO, WORLD

Edited by Linda Jay Editing Services

Printed and bound by Lorna Johnson Print

Printed in China in 2018

CPSIA: Lorna Johnson Print | Job #18-610 | Production Date November 2018 | Shenzhen, China

Published by Big Ideas For Small People

P.O. Box 789

Los Gatos, CA 95031

ISBN

978-0-9997252-0-7

ToSiliconValleyAndBeyond.com

BIG IDEAS
FOR SMALL PEOPLE

My goal in writing this book was to create an appealing local children's picture book with a global message. I love meaningful children's picture books that deliver food for thought in a simple way. This book is meant to be an interesting read for all ages. For example, with little kids, you can just follow the story on a basic level. My goal is to get parents and kids to talk about the topics—to learn from each other and keep a vibrant connection to each other when it comes to technology. I would love to spark an interest and inspire you to research further.

Chances are, you live in Silicon Valley, know someone who lives here, or use a product or service that originates here. Acquiring more in-depth knowledge about the history of this place enhances your experience. Most of all, I am a big proponent of nurturing creativity and passion in children. The secret of success is not just early enrichment and parental coaching. Successful Silicon Valley entrepreneurs have other factors in their mindset in common: a positive attitude toward failure, an openness to the opportunities of the moment, the overall goal of improving the world, the ability to connect the dots and see the bigger picture, and the ability to collaborate to bring the best ideas together. Silicon Valley is about great ideas. This book is about enabling every person to have a growth mindset for success in a very sustainable and fulfilling way.

Enjoy the journey!
Andrea Anderson

Trixie, her brother Ben, and their parents live in Silicon Valley, that high-tech place buzzing with excitement. Most people around the world have heard of "The Valley."

Where exactly is Silicon Valley? Let's take a look at our map.

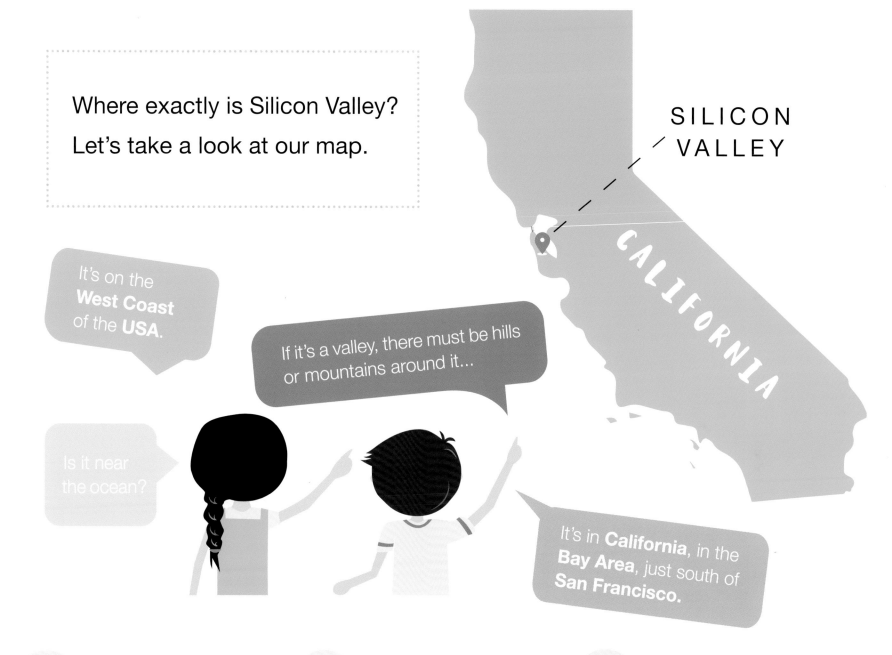

1 — DID YOU KNOW?

Silicon Valley is the nickname for the southern part of the San Francisco Bay Area. San Jose is considered "the capital" of Silicon Valley.

2 — GOOD TO KNOW

Silicon is the chemical element used to make computer chips, which was the first major technology industry in Silicon Valley. Silicon is found in sand and rocks.

3 — REALLY?

Other cities in Silicon Valley are Palo Alto, Cupertino, Los Gatos, Los Altos, Saratoga, Sunnyvale, Mountain View, Menlo Park, Campbell, and Santa Clara. They have all grown together into one big populated area that keeps expanding.

In Silicon Valley, virtual places become real! People in countries all over the world connect with virtual places simply by turning on their computers.

"Vir-tu-al" means "not physically existing as such but made by software to appear to exist."

Seems pretty real to me most of the time...

So, if something exists only on your computer, is it real or not?

...and the computer certainly impacts your real life!

4 DID YOU KNOW?

The first email ever was sent on ARPAnet by Ray Tomlinson, an American computer programmer, in 1971. ARPAnet was renamed "the Internet" in 1984 and email became widely used in the 1990s.

5 DO YOU REMEMBER?

The HP Garage in Palo Alto is considered the birthplace of Silicon Valley. William Hewlett and David Packard founded their technology company here in 1939.

6 FUN FACT

The very first website went live on August 6, 1991. It was a website about the World Wide Web. The creator, Sir Timothy Berners-Lee, is the first "Internaut."

A lot has changed in Silicon Valley over the years: Native Americans, Spanish missionaries, Gold Rush adventurers, fruit pickers, and computer engineers have impacted "The Valley" in many ways.

I guess life is all about change...

Yes, **Albert Einstein** said: "Life is like riding a bicycle. In order to keep your balance, you must keep moving."

Are you saying life is all about cycling??

LET'S VISIT THE PAST TO UNDERSTAND THE PRESENT!

 To go straight to the present, skip the next page.

GOLD RUSH

The Gold Rush in 1848 attracted gold seekers from many parts of the world. Many stayed even after the gold had been mined.

Gold was found at Sutter's Mill in Coloma, near Sacramento, on January 24, 1848. John Sutter and James Marshall tried to keep it a secret—but eventually 300,000 gold seekers came.

Gold seekers came by ship or wagon train: The argonauts' sailing voyage from the East Coast to the West Coast went around the tip of South America and took five to eight months. Most overlanders came in wagon trains on the Oregon Trail and California Trail. The gold seekers were called the 49ers, as in 1849—just like the famous football team.

> You sure could. Even more so, you could strike it rich if you kept adapting.

> You could strike it rich with GOLD!

> ????

> There was actually not that much gold to be found, but plenty of business opportunities. The story goes that Levi Strauss invented jeans out of tent material.

> This is a much more pleasant way of traveling across the country than walking on the Oregon Trail.

TRANSCONTINENTAL RAILROAD

California became the 31st state in the USA in 1850 and got connected to the other states by the Transcontinental Railroad.

The Transcontinental Railroad was built to connect the East Coast with the West Coast. It was a 1,912-mile-long railroad line to the San Francisco Bay. Sacramento's significance started with Sutter's Fort and the Gold Rush. Today it is California's state capital. Before that, San Jose, Vallejo, Benicia, and San Francisco were capitals of California for short periods of time.

THE OHLONE INDIANS

The Ohlone Indians were the first known Native Americans in this part of California.

The Ohlone, also known as Costanoans, lived in the area for 3,000 years. Most of their food was made from acorns. They ate an abundance of roots, seeds, and grasses as well as insects, reptiles, rodents, birds, fish, and larger game animals. Little went to waste. Sharing and friendship were important values in the Ohlone communities. There was no broad division between rich and poor.

> Imagine you lived all in sync with nature!

> Somehow nostalgic!

> It's very impressive that adobe bricks last this long.

> There were 21 missions along the coast of California. You can still visit many of them.

> Actually, most missions were rebuilt or significantly repaired.

MISSIONS

When the Spanish conquered the coast of "Alta California," many Natives started living in the missions that were being built. Mission Santa Clara de Asís gave Santa Clara County its name.

Mission Santa Clara was founded on January 12, 1777, by Junipero Serra. It was the eighth mission in California and the first to be named after a woman. Santa Clara of Assisi and San Francisco were the saints of the poor. They were very popular saints in the 1700s—a bit like celebrities today!

PAST

PRESENT

TECHNOLOGY

Semiconductors made electronics possible.
The HP Garage is considered the birthplace of Silicon Valley.

Bill Hewlett and Dave Packard were freshmen in the same student dormitory at Stanford in the 1930s. The two built the first audio oscillator, the HP200A, a device that generates a tone, or frequency. Their breakthrough happened when Disney bought eight of them for the film *Fantasia*. The HP Garage in Palo Alto, where they tinkered with their inventions, is referred to as the "birthplace of Silicon Valley."

William Shockley was the co-founder of the first semiconductor business. He settled in Mountain View in the 1950s because he wanted to live near his aging, ill mother. This brought technology from the East Coast to the West Coast. In 1957, eight skilled, young executives left Shockley because working conditions were not good at all. The "traitorous eight" believed in the future of developing semiconductors and founded Fairchild Semiconductor. Numerous influential Silicon Valley companies can be traced back to Fairchild, lovingly called the "Fairchildren."

It's almost like a second Gold Rush.

SILICON VALLEY

In the late 1950s, Dr. Frederick Terman was the dean of the School of Engineering at Stanford University. He gave his students the opportunity to build their inventions and try them out in the lab.

The novelty of Terman's approach lay in turning ideas from academia into real products and businesses. Still today, Stanford's Engineering Department has the Product Realization Lab in Room 36. All students can come and build their inventions here. Various start-up incubators, like StartX or the Y Combinator, help students turn their ideas into businesses. The founders of Google, Yahoo, Netflix, Cisco, Intel, Nike, and Trader Joe's were all students at Stanford at some point.

I like it! Inventing is thinking and making!

STANFORD

Leland and Jane Stanford founded Stanford University in 1885 in honor of their son. Leland Junior died of typhoid fever in Italy at the age of 15 when he was traveling in Europe with his parents.

The university was built on Leland Stanford's previous Palo Alto farm. "Palo Alto" means "tall tree," in reference to a giant California redwood tree by the San Francisquito Creek. It is the centerpiece of Stanford's official seal. Education at Stanford was free until 1920.

With no other children of their own, Leland and Jane Stanford decided to give the gift of education to ALL the children of California. They founded Stanford University.

That is so sad and so fortunate at the same time.

5

6

VALLEY OF HEART'S DELIGHT

Until the 1960s, the Santa Clara Valley produced more fruit than any other region in the world.

This is delicious!

Prunes, almonds, apricots, peaches, and cherries were the main fruits produced in Santa Clara Valley. It was known as the "Valley of Heart's Delight" and the "Prune Capital of America." The first orchards were planted by the Spanish missionaries in the garden of the Mission of Santa Clara! The long, dry summers and mild winters made for ideal growing conditions.

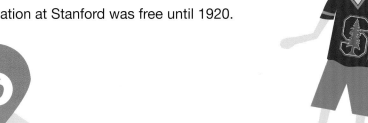

Come and join us on a tour of today's Silicon Valley to visit the companies that started and grew here!

How do we create a memorable tour through the valley of computers and creators?

LET'S SEARCH GOOGLE!
EVEN BETTER, LET'S CHECK OUT GOOGLE'S HEADQUARTERS.

So, how do we actually get into the world of Google? You can't just walk into offices unless you have an employee badge. Google is a real work place, not a tourist attraction. Let's do 21st-century sightseeing and "Google" our way in.

At first, there wasn't much information on the web at all. Then content expanded. **Search engines** came on the scene to help people find what they were looking for.

So cool that although **"Google"** is a made-up word from the 1990s, now people all over the world know what it refers to.

You can see lots of people riding colorful Google bikes between their Google offices. If you are lucky, you see their self-driving car Waymo and Google Earth cars with street-view cameras. Visit the Googleplex to absorb the atmosphere of a company with an innovative work culture.

If you are after some branded souvenirs and gadgets, go to the Google Merchandise Store nearby.

It's amazing how an **internet search engine** evolves into other areas of life.

I like your creative mind, Inventorix! Maybe Darwin would stick with e-volution?

Would Darwin describe this as the "webolution"?

GOOGLE BIKE

WAYMO

7 DID YOU KNOW?

"Baby Google," in the basement of the Huang Engineering Center at Stanford University, is the first server that Larry Page and Sergey Brin built in 1996. They built the housing structure out of LEGO bricks. The bright colors were the inspiration for the Google branding.

8 WOW

A "googol" is the number 1 followed by 100 zeros. "Google" is a play on this word, referencing the massive amounts of information that can be searched.

9 FUN FACT

According to Google, Waymo stands for "a new way forward in mobility." The goal of self-driving cars is to make the roads safer. Waymo belongs to Google's parent company, Alphabet.

Wow, I didn't realize that so many real people work for something that is "just" on my computer.

Google, or any other search engine, doesn't "know" the answers. The Googlers program their search engine to find the most likely answers from all the information on the Internet.

Search 🔍

What do they all do?

10 FUN FACT

Google was formally incorporated in a garage in September 1998 in Menlo Park. Garage startups are a big part of Silicon Valley's story!

11 DID YOU KNOW?

In 2006, the verb "google" was added into dictionaries!

12 DID YOU KNOW?

Google's innovative culture led to the development of multiple other businesses. Their parent company Alphabet was formed in 2015.

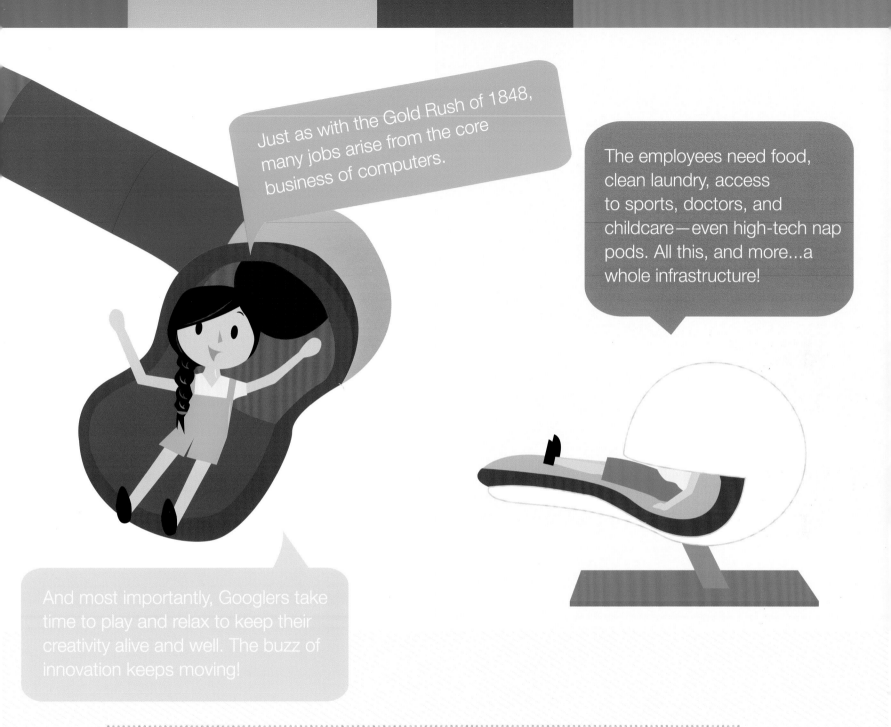

Inspired by all that rolling motion at Google, let's take a detour from computers to check out high-tech cars at Tesla, Silicon Valley's pioneering electric car company.

ON THE MOVE!

The desire to transform and improve a traditional product is what Tesla, Inc. has in common with other Silicon Valley companies. With no prior experience in building cars, Tesla built an electric car.

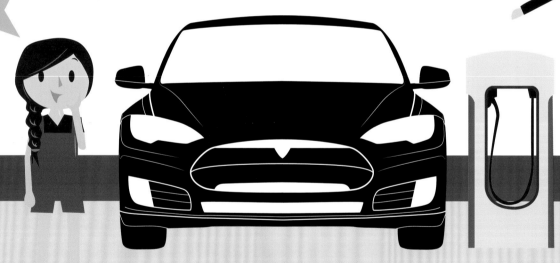

It takes a determined mind to make change happen!

How far can I drive with this car?

Is this supercharger my refueling station???

13 DID YOU KNOW?

Elon Musk is not only CEO of Tesla, Inc., but involved in many entrepreneurial ventures including PayPal, SpaceX, Neuralink, OpenAI, and the Boring Company.

14 TUBULAR!

At the Boring Company, Elon Musk is working on the hyperloop—a transportation system to send people traveling in a pressurized tube. A trip from San Francisco to Los Angeles would take half an hour.

15 EXTRATERRESTRIAL

SpaceX revolutionizes space technology with the goal of enabling people to live on other planets and travel into space. The first landing on Mars is planned for the 2020s.

The concept is more than just a car. Tesla transforms solar energy into electricity, which then powers cars and more. For now, a Tesla drives semi-autonomously. When will the cars ask us where we want to be driven next? The race to develop self-driving and electric cars has expanded to the entire world.

16 REALLY?

Sunshine gives us energy! Solar roof tiles that collect energy for our house and car let us use a renewable resource.

17 WOW!

Will artificial intelligence (AI) work for us or against us? As AI becomes smarter and more influential, OpenAI and an ethics commission want to ensure that humans stay safe.

Do you think that self-driving cars will be our new normal at the end of the decade?

The days when apple and blackberry were thought of as just fruits are definitely over.

Let's follow the clues! Will Apple's map icon take us to an actual place?

Wow, my sister turns into an iconic web detective!

I have a feeling I know where we will end up!

Apple's headquarters at 1 Apple Park Way are just off I-280, which runs through Silicon Valley.

18 DID YOU KNOW?

Steve Jobs and Steve Wozniak became friends in high school. They shared a love for technology and playing pranks.

19 REALLY?

The first iPhone was released on June 29, 2007. It was revolutionary because it combined an iPod, a mobile phone, and an internet communications device all in one.

20 NICE TO KNOW

An infinite loop is an endlessly-circling sequence of program instructions. For about 25 years, 1 Infinite Loop was Apple's famous headquarters, often called "The Mothership."

Would you be surprised to learn that we can get inside Apple Park only if we work there? The good news is that Apple has an extensive visitor center worth visiting. Apart from the company store selling Apple products and merchandise, you can actually "peek" into the campus. A 3D model gives you a bird's-eye view of the campus. With the help of iPads and augmented reality, we can embark on our virtual journey inside.

I see apple trees along with apricot, olive, and cherry trees, like in the olden days of "The Valley."

It links the journey of Silicon Valley from orchards to garages to major enterprises!

This is like working in a spaceship! And it's all energy efficient.

This place is built where HP used to have their headquarters. Today's biggest HQ on Earth rests on the spot of Silicon Valley's founding fathers' HQ.

In our imagination, we can see Steve Jobs' vision inspiring him to create this company. The **perseverance** and **effort** it took to develop the first computers. The **grit** to keep going, even when it seemed impossible to succeed. The **passion** to make something happen that no one had ever imagined.

PASSION	EFFORT	PERSEVERANCE	GRIT
A strong feeling of enthusiasm	Energy used to do something	Continuing to do something even though it is difficult	Mental toughness and courage

Human connection used to happen only in person. But with the use of technology, we can now stay connected even to those who are not close to us physically.

LET'S STAY CONNECTED

21 DID YOU KNOW?

Some people have "friends" online that they don't even know in real life! As social beings, humans need friendships to be happy.

22 REALLY?

Through technology, people all over the world can get access to knowledge and education.

23 GOOD TO KNOW

Mark Zuckerberg created Facebook when he was a student at Harvard University. The idea was to connect students with each other. On February 4, 2004, he launched "TheFacebook" and later named it "Facebook."

Ready to virtually check on what our friends are up to? One click on Facebook will usually do it. Today, we will make our way to Facebook's headquarters at "Hacker Way."

A photo with the famous "Thumbs Up" is the most we get at Hacker Way. Google your way inside to see more!

I like it.

Hacker! What a cool name.

Remember: Don't just count your connections; make your connections count!

1 Hacker Way

It's somehow weird that you find out more about Facebook on the web than by being here in real life!

24 DID YOU KNOW?

Instagram, WhatsApp, and Oculus VR are all part of Facebook! Continuing to innovate is the way to keep up.

25 REALLY?

On the back of the Facebook sign at the entrance is the company sign of Sun Microsystems, which was located at that site before Facebook. Mark Zuckerberg renovated the entire campus. He decided to preserve the original sign to remind people of the history of Silicon Valley.

I WANT IT NOW!!

Online shopping removes many shopping limitations: Closing times? Not applicable. Limited item choice? Unlikely. Driving around for hours to compare prices? A convenient click will do the job. Carrying heavy shopping bags home? Only from your front door!

Are you ready for an eBay shopping stroll? Of course, there is no actual eBay shopping mall in Silicon Valley. Again, you'll only find office buildings with the familiar eBay logo. Stop by their visitor center to learn more!

Well, with the internet there is an endless supply of temptations on the web...

So, I shouldn't chill out on the sofa all day and browse the shops?

Note to self: use navigation system of self-navigation... noted....GPS programmed! Frequent reminders might be necessary...

And the more there is on offer, the more I need to develop good judgment to make wise choices.

CHECK OUT

Pay with credit card, PayPal, or giftcard.
Review, confirm, and pay.

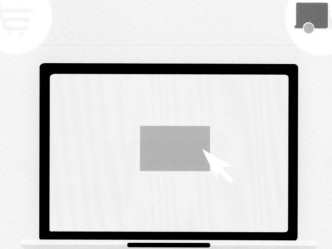

ADD TO CART

Click to put item(s) into
your shopping basket.

TRACK YOUR PACKAGE

Go online to check where your
package is.

SEARCH

What product do you need
or want?

DELIVERY

You get your package!

26 · SPARK AN IDEA

In 1995, the first item ever listed on eBay was a broken laser pointer, which sold for $14.83. Pierre Omidyar listed it as a test and was surprised that it actually sold! The man who bought it told Pierre Omidyar he collected broken laser pointers.

27 · REALLY?

Gumtree, Stubhub, and Skype are all eBay companies.

28 · GOOD TO KNOW

eBay was originally called Auction Web. Pierre Omidyar went live with the site on Labor Day weekend in 1995. eBay started purely with auctions and bidding. Today, most sales are "Buy It Now."

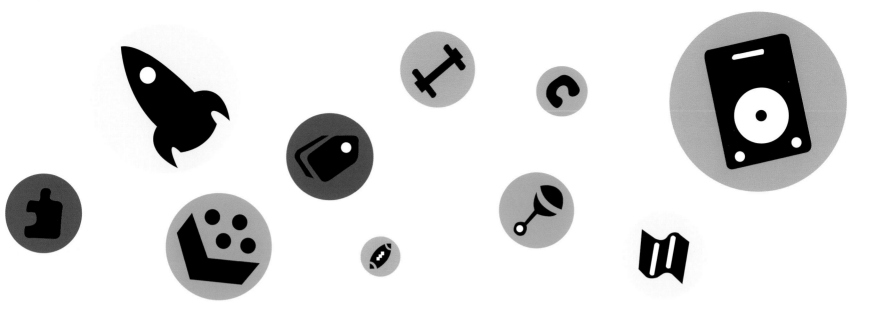

The significance and potential of eBay is its web presence and the possibilities for every user in the world. The responsibility to stay connected with reality also is in every user. Make your choices wisely in a world full of possibilities!

Nearly anything has been sold on eBay—from clothing to toys, electronics, jewelry, sporting goods, and more. Even the original Hollywood sign was sold on eBay!

Anyone can sell anything from anywhere on eBay. YOU can be a business person!

Find out how auctions are held in a traditional auction house.

WHO IS WATCHING?

TRIXIE

BEN A.K.A INVENTORIX

ADD PROFILE

Do you remember VHS or DVD rental?

Or waiting for your favorite TV show to continue a week later?

Then you are a kid from the pre-Netflix times!

Online streaming became possible through big data transmission in the internet age. Netflix is another example of a practical startup idea that made it big and has a global impact.

31 ARE YOU NEXT?

With high-quality phones and personal computers to film and edit movies, any of us could make good-quality movies. YouTube lets anyone publish. With some luck, your movie might make it onto Netflix!

32 CAN YOU IMAGINE?

TV and movie theaters used to be the only screens where you could watch something. What would your life be like if you weren't watching on a phone, tablet, or computer?

33 MORE TO KNOW

Hollywood has been the center of moviemaking for over a hundred years. More and more special effects are created through computer generated imaging (CGI) and rendering. Much of the CGI created today is made with technology from Silicon Valley.

Let's make our last stop at Intel. Inside, visitors are welcomed to a free history museum that teaches about the first microprocessors, binary code, and what a "clean room" is. You can embark on a decade-long journey of innovation and get a good clue about where Silicon Valley got its name.

34 — MICRO FACT

A microchip, or integrated circuit, is a thin slice of silicon with many transistors chemically printed into it to create an entire electrical circuit!

35 — THE BEGINNING

Gordon Moore and Robert Noyce co-founded Fairchild Semiconductor (1957) and Intel (1968). They created the microprocessor, which we use today in every electronic device.

36 — FUNNY FACT

A speck of dust falling on a microprocessor is comparable to a grand piano falling on a person! Microchips must be fabricated in cleanrooms where dust is filtered out of the air. Technicians wear special lab suits, nicknamed "bunny suits."

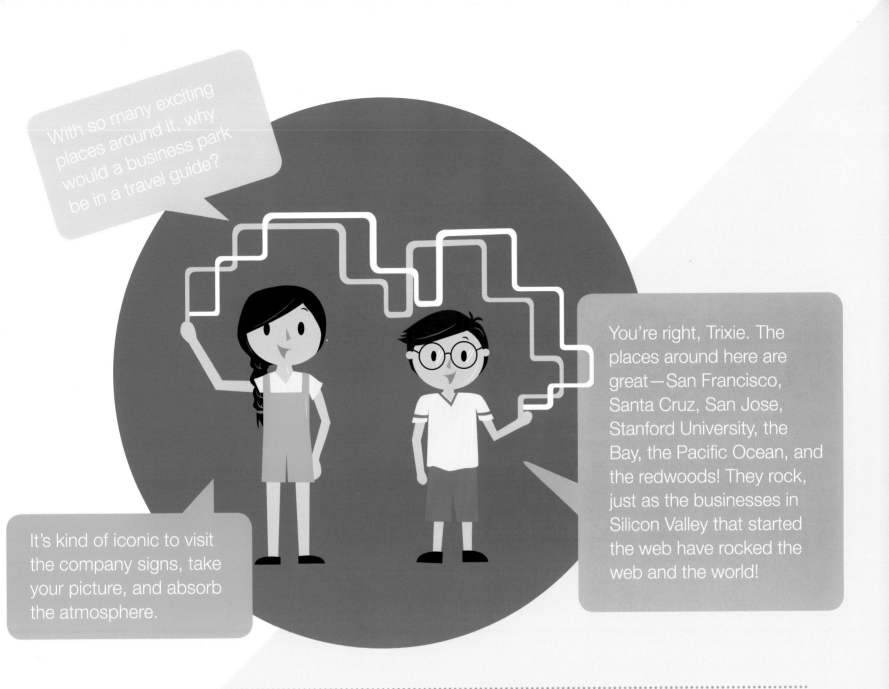

We are starting to realize that there are real places in Silicon Valley that you can actually visit, even though they haven't yet appeared much in travel guides.

MINDSET

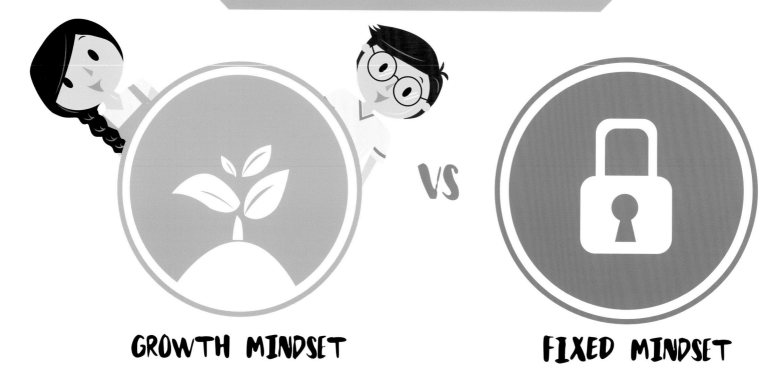

GROWTH MINDSET

VS

FIXED MINDSET

Most of all, Silicon Valley is a mindset.

Inventors, entrepreneurs, and businesspeople here have open, curious minds that believe in growth and innovation. They share the desire to create something that finds its way into people's lives—something nobody thought they would need or miss.

"Whether you think you can or think you can't, you are right."
- **Henry Ford**

"An honest, open environment can bring out the best in people."
- **Pierre Omidyar**

"Great companies start because the founders want to change the world, not make a fast buck."
- **Guy Kawasaki**

The Silicon Valley mindset represents visionaries who connect with each other, develop ideas, pursue thoughts, persevere with their plans, learn from mistakes, and never stop searching and creating.

Unlike explorers in the old days who discovered and then conquered places that were already there, Silicon Valley explorers imagine things that are not in the world yet and then turn them into reality.

"The biggest risk is not taking any risk."
- **Mark Zuckerberg**

"I'm convinced that about half of what separates successful entrepreneurs from the non-successful ones is pure perseverance."
- **Steve Jobs**

"The only thing worse than starting something and failing is not starting something."
- **Seth Godin**

PASSION

Passion has always sparked exploration. Even today, it is still passion and enthusiasm that keep curiosity alive and lead to the most unlikely and creative inventions.

"At the core of Silicon Valley is a passion for 'yes.'"
- Steven Levy

"Great minds discuss ideas; average minds discuss events; small minds discuss people."
- Eleanor Roosevelt

"It is the ultimate luxury to combine passion and contribution. It's also a very clear path to happiness."
- Sheryl Sandberg

CREATIVITY

Did you know that everybody is creative?

Sure! Creativity develops by being creative. It's like a muscle that you train.

And it's so much fun!

Ok, let's figure out what we will make...!

Yes, let's keep training our creativity and have fun!

"To have a great idea, have a lot of them."
- **Thomas Edison**

"Every great dream begins with a dreamer. Always remember, you have within you the strength, the patience, and the passion to reach for the stars to change the world."
- **Harriet Tubman**

"Creativity is intelligence having fun."
- **Albert Einstein**

Take a journey to the most amazing place in the world: your own imagination and creativity! Maybe the joy of exploring your own possibilities will take you to Silicon Valley—or maybe it will take you to a totally new place that nobody has thought of yet. You can be the one who carries the spirit of Silicon Valley elsewhere!

WHO'S WHO?

ANDREA ANDERSON

Andrea is the creative mind behind lots of ideas. In her parenting classes she empowers parents to make their children and families thrive. Her research focus is creativity, Silicon Valley mindset, innovation, giftedness, history, and what makes a meaningful life. Andrea grew up in Germany, lived in London for 10 years, and moved to Silicon Valley with her family in 2010.

MONICA SHEHATA

Monica is currently studying graphic design and interactive arts at California Polytechnic State University, San Luis Obispo. Monica grew up living in different parts of the world, including Egypt and Oman. She enjoys traveling the world and outdoor activities such as hiking, rock climbing, and scuba diving.

UYEN VICKY VO

Vicky changes as fast as the Silicon Valley startup culture. During her studies, she was in charge of designing print and digital materials for West Valley College while pursuing a degree in digital media as well as web and mobile design.
Originally from Vietnam, she came to California at the age of 15. This is when her interests in design and technology started. Vicky has the openness and curiosity of a true Silicon Valley girl and is involved in various startups.

Saint Clare of Assisi (1194-1253): Italian saint and follower of Saint Francis of Assisi

Saint Francis of Assisi (ca.1181-1226): Italian friar and saint

Sir Timothy Berners-Lee (1955-): British computer scientist; CERN, wrote first URL, HTTP, and HTML

Sergey Brin (1973-): Russian-born American computer scientist and internet entrepreneur, co-founder of Google

Charles Darwin (1809-1882): English naturalist, geologist and biologist, science of evolution

Thomas Edison (1847-1931): Known as America's greatest inventor; electric light, motion picture camera

Albert Einstein (1879-1955): German-born American theoretical physicist

Henry Ford (1863-1947): Founder of Ford Motor Company

Seth Godin (1960-): American author and entrepreneur

Reed Hastings (1960-): American entrepreneur and philanthropist, co-founder of Netflix

William Hewlett (1913-2001): American engineer and co-founder of Hewlett-Packard Company

Steve Jobs (1955-2011): American entrepreneur and co-founder of Apple

Guy Kawasaki (1954-): American marketing specialist, author, Silicon Valley venture capitalist

Steven Levy (1951-): American technology journalist and author

James Marshall (1810-1885): Sawmill operator who found gold at Sutter's Fort

Gordon Moore (1929-): Co-founder of Intel, author of Moore's law, one of the "traitorous eight"

Elon Musk (1971-): South African-born Canadian-American engineer and inventor, Tesla

Robert Noyce (1927-1990): Co-founder of Fairchild Semiconductor and Intel, "The Mayor of Silicon Valley," "traitorous eight"

Pierre Omidyar (1967-): French-Iranian-American entrepreneur, founder of eBay

David Packard (1912-1996): American electrical engineer and co-founder of HP

Larry Page (1973-): American computer scientist and internet entrepreneur, co-founder of Google

Marc Randolph (1958-): American tech entrepreneur, co-founder of Netflix

Eleanor Roosevelt (1884-1962): First Lady of the United States, politician, diplomat, and activist

Sheryl Sandberg (1969-): COO of Facebook, author and philanthropist

Junipero Serra (1713-1784): Roman Catholic Spanish priest, founder of nine missions in California

William Shockley (1910-1989): American physicist and inventor, manager at Bell Labs

Jane Stanford (1828-1905): Co-founder of Stanford University

Leland Stanford (1824-1893): Entrepreneur, politician, co-founder of Stanford University

Leland Stanford Junior (1868-1884): Only child of Jane and Leland Stanford in whose memory Stanford University was founded

John Sutter (1803-1880): German-born Swiss pioneer, Gold Rush started at Sutter's Fort

Frederick Terman (1900-1982): American engineer and dean of the School of Engineering at Stanford, "Father of Silicon Valley"

Ray Tomlinson (1941-2016): American computer programmer who invented the first email program

Harriet Tubman (ca.1822-1913): Former enslaved leader who became an icon of American courage and freedom

Steve Wozniak (1950-): Pioneer of the personal computer revolution, co-founder of Apple

Mark Zuckerberg (1984-): American internet entrepreneur, co-founder of Facebook

References and disclaimers:

A Journey to Silicon Valley and Beyond is an independent book publication and has no affiliation, sponsorship, or endorsement by any company, town, or person in the book. The book's sole purpose is to inspire, inform, and entertain readers.

To the best of our knowledge and understanding, company pages are created within the guidelines of their rules for proper usage of their logos and trademarks. The companies have been informed about the book project and given opportunity for feedback and change.

Rubik's Cube® used by permission of Rubik's Brand Ltd.

All trademarks are the property of their respective companies/owners.

Images in the book have been created by our graphic designers, and in a few cases, purchased from Shutterstock.

THANK YOU FOR YOUR PART IN MY JOURNEY!

Writing a book is not a one-person enterprise. Maybe the first draft is—but so much inspiration from the people and world around us goes into the first draft. Once the first draft is there, it takes a village to make this into a printed book. It takes a village to keep going. I don't recall for how long the idea for this book lived with us now, but it's been a while. Perhaps, my kids will always associate their childhood in California with A Journey to Silicon Valley and Beyond. Thank you to my family, Gordon, Max, Julius, and Victoria for your endless support and patience; Gordon, for moving to California with me. Without the move, the idea for the book wouldn't have been born. I was looking for a book about Silicon Valley for our family and it didn't exist. So, I had to write it myself. Thank you to my mother and grandmother for sparking an interest in the history of the place we live in. Years ago, they have written about their hometown in past and present. Kids, thank you for letting me chaperone on field trips in your elementary school years where I got inspired with interesting facts about Silicon Valley. I was the adult who was always taking notes. Thank you, Julius, for being my social media manager and early image designer. Indeed, Julius and Victoria illustrated the earliest version of this book—time to dig that out. This book started as a project to make our kids grow. In the end, they published their own book in school much faster than I did. Thank you, Julius, for the gift of your time to go on tours to explore Silicon Valley. Some of the explorations can be seen on our Instagram feed. Thank you, Max, for your memes that kept us entertained. Thank you, Victoria, for questioning so much, which made us improve the project. Thank you to our local schools, Project Cornerstone, and Parenting Continuum for broadening my understanding about developing worthwhile educational goals. Thank you to Stanford's teachings about growth mindset and all the good lessons I learned through Challenge Success, Carol Dweck, and Jo Boaler. Thank you to fourth grade for teaching me such interesting local history. Thank you California travel guides from 1991 for not having any information about Silicon Valley in you. You really made me want to find out more. It only took me 20 years to come back and do so! Thank you to the colleges and universities in Silicon Valley to let me put up flyers to find an illustrator and graphic designer. Thank you to all the students who applied. Special thank you to Vicky and Monica who have worked with me on this project for over a year and created a beautiful result, displayed amazing perseverance and work attitude. Any future employer of these two talented ladies can consider themselves lucky. I loved working with them and hope our endeavors bring us together again. Thank you to my fellow authors at Bay Area Independent Publishers (BAIPA) in Marin County for sharing experiences and expertise about self-publishing. Thank you, Linda and Lorna, my editor and printing agent I found at BAIPA. Thank you to my local editor friends who helped me with refining the story, spotting the remaining typos, and discussing lots of comma options and capitalization decisions. Being German, I like to capitalize a lot of nouns and needed some convincing to change that. Being German, I also thought there are fixed rules for punctuation and I had no appreciation that I could pick which rules to follow to make punctuation decisions. Thank you to the Silicon Valley companies who created the devices and technology that I am using to do all this. Thank you to our local Apple Store in Los Gatos to teach me in endless patience how to make the most out of my Mac and how to use all the features. It helps so much to use your tools with ease when you work on a product. Thank you to the person next to me at Starbucks who encouraged me to do a Kickstarter campaign. And thank you to all the Kickstarters who made it a success, believed in the project, and supported me. Thank you, Sir Tim Berners-Lee for inventing the internet so that I could search for facts easily. Research in the library during my times as a student was so much more time-consuming! Thank you to all who develop the internet further and add an abundance of great content and features. Thank you for all the friendly staff at the companies and visitor centers of Silicon Valley companies. Your outgoing, welcoming, and informative attitude are amazing. Some of your stories are so precious—they might make my next book. Thank you to friends who took me on the campus of their companies. Looking behind the closed doors is amazing, but still, this book is about what you can explore when you don't have that special access. Thank you to all of you who buy this book, read this book, give this book to their relatives in their home countries, enjoy this book, and get inspiration from the ideas in this book.

ENJOY THE JOURNEY!